Junior
Guest Spot

KIDS TV THEMES

easy playalong for violin

WISE PUBLICATIONS
part of The Music Sales Group
London/New York/Paris/Sydney/Copenhagen/Berlin/Madrid/Tokyo

For ease of play, the key and tempo of some of
the themes in this book do not necessarily match
editions of this title for other instruments. Such pieces,
therefore, will not be suitable for group playing using
different instruments.

Published by
Wise Publications
8/9 Frith Street,
London W1D 3JB, England.

Exclusive Distributors:
Music Sales Limited
Distribution Centre, Newmarket Road,
Bury St. Edmunds, Suffolk IP33 3YB, England.

Music Sales Pty Limited
120 Rothschild Avenue,
Rosebery, NSW 2018, Australia.

Order No. AM973588
ISBN 0-7119-9269-X
This book © Copyright 2003 by Wise Publications.

Music arranged by Simon Lesley.
Music processed by Enigma Music Production Services.
Cover photography courtesy George Taylor.
Printed in the United Kingdom by
Printwise (Haverhill) Limited, Haverhill, Suffolk.

CD recorded, mixed and mastered by Jonas Persson.
Instrumental solos by Dermot Crehan.
Backing tracks arranged by Danny Gluckstein.

Your Guarantee of Quality:
As publishers, we strive to produce every book to
the highest commercial standards.
The music has been freshly engraved and the book
has been carefully designed to minimise awkward page
turns and to make playing from it a real pleasure.
Particular care has been given to specifying acid-free,
neutral-sized paper made from pulps which have not
been elemental chlorine bleached.
This pulp is from farmed sustainable forests and
was produced with special regard for the environment.
Throughout, the printing and binding have been planned
to ensure a sturdy, attractive publication which should
give years of enjoyment.
If your copy fails to meet our high standards,
please inform us and we will gladly replace it.

www.musicsales.com

Captain Pugwash 6

Chatterhappy Ponies 10

Pingu 11

Pokemon Theme 12

Postman Pat 14

Roobarb & Custard 17

Rugrats 18

Sesame Street Theme 24

Sooty Theme 20

The Wombling Song 22

CAPTAIN PUGWASH

Traditional
Arranged by Gordon Lorenz

9

CHATTERHAPPY PONIES

By Peter Gosling

PINGU

By Antonio Conde

POKEMON THEME

Words & Music by Tamara Loffler & John Siegler

POSTMAN PAT

Words & Music by Bryan Daly

ROOBARB & CUSTARD

By Mark Pritchard & Johnny Hawksworth

RUGRATS

By Mark Mothersbaugh

SOOTY THEME

By Harry Corbett

THE WOMBLING SONG

Words & Music by Mike Batt

SESAME STREET THEME

Words & Music by Joe Raposo, Jon Stone & Bruce Hart